WHSmith

Progress Tests

Maths

Steve Mills and Hilary Koll

Age 6–7
Year 2
Key Stage 1

Hachette UK's policy is to use papers that are natural, renewable and recyclable products and made from wood grown in sustainable forests. The logging and manufacturing processes are expected to conform to the environmental regulations of the country of origin.

Orders: please contact Bookpoint Ltd, 130 Milton Park, Abingdon, Oxon OX14 4SB. Telephone: (44) 01235 827720. Fax: (44) 01235 400454. Lines are open 9.00a.m.–5.00p.m., Monday to Saturday, with a 24-hour message answering service. Visit our website at www.hoddereducation.co.uk.

First published in 2013 exclusively for WHSmith by
Hodder Education
An Hachette UK Company
Carmelite House, 50 Victoria Embankment
London EC4Y 0DZ

Impression number 10 9 8 7 6 5
Year 2020 2019 2018

This edition has been updated, 2014, to reflect National Curriculum changes.

Cover illustration by Oxford Designers and Illustrators Ltd
Illustrations by Fakenham Prepress Solutions, Fakenham, Norfolk NR21 8NN
Typeset in 16pt Folio by Fakenham Prepress Solutions, Fakenham, Norfolk NR21 8NN
Printed in Dubai

A catalogue record for this title is available from the British Library.

ISBN: 978 1444 188 240

Introduction

How this book can help your child

This book contains practice of the essential areas of mathematics expected of children aged 6–7. Each of the Progress Tests covers a key area, including number work, measurement, shape and space work and data handling.

This book provides opportunity for testing children's knowledge, skills and understanding of these key areas. Regular practice helps children to build a good mathematical foundation and to gain confidence in all aspects of the curriculum.

How to use this book

To get the most from this book:

- Encourage your child to take the tests regularly, ideally one per day.
- Read the first question aloud in different ways e.g. use the words 'add, plus' etc. to help your child recognise what to do, e.g. whether to add, double or take away.
- Time each test. As your child becomes more confident, the time should decrease.
- If the early tests take more than 15 minutes to complete, suggest that your child tackles a section at a time with a break in-between.
- Involve your child in marking the tests and talk together about any incorrect answers. Be sensitive and draw more attention to those that were correct, asking your child to tell you how they tackled the question and what they found difficult about it.
- When the marks for the tests are added up, the results may be recorded on the record sheet (on the inside back cover). This will give you and the children a sense of how well they are doing.
- Draw attention to improvements made in the times or marks.
- Praise and encourage your child at all stages.

Test 1: Numbers to 100

Write these numbers in words.

1. 48
2. 52
3. 67
4. 44
5. 59
6. 93
7. 86

Write these as numbers.

8. ninety-seven
9. twenty-one
10. sixty-eight
11. eighty-seven
12. seventy
13. forty-five
14. seventeen

Mark your answers. How well did you do?

Mark ☐ out of 14 Time taken ☐

Test 2: Place value

Write the value of each underlined digit.

1. $\underline{4}7$ ☐
2. $5\underline{8}$ ☐
3. $\underline{5}3$ ☐
4. $7\underline{2}$ ☐
5. $\underline{6}8$ ☐
6. $\underline{8}2$ ☐
7. $3\underline{6}$ ☐
8. $\underline{7}8$ ☐

Partition these numbers into tens and units.

9. 82 = ☐ + ☐
10. 97 = ☐ + ☐
11. 61 = ☐ + ☐
12. 76 = ☐ + ☐

Write the totals.

13. 60 + 7 = ☐
14. 40 + 3 = ☐
15. 20 + 8 = ☐

Mark your answers. How well did you do?

Mark ☐ out of 15 Time taken ☐

Test 3: Comparing and ordering

Tick the larger number in each pair.

1. 47 ☐ 19 ☐
2. 63 ☐ 78 ☐
3. 88 ☐ 51 ☐
4. 59 ☐ 98 ☐
5. 82 ☐ 69 ☐
6. 92 ☐ 50 ☐
7. 78 ☐ 87 ☐
8. 93 ☐ 92 ☐

Put the numbers in order, smallest first.

9. 82, 32, 14, 25 ☐
10. 21, 76, 8, 50, 27 ☐
11. 89, 73, 96, 62, 9 ☐
12. 55, 42, 54, 52, 25 ☐

Put the numbers in order, largest first.

13. 86, 43, 17, 60, 100 ☐
14. 92, 98, 94, 7, 76, 17 ☐
15. 12, 58, 25, 89, 85 ☐

Mark your answers. How well did you do?

Mark ☐ out of 15 Time taken ☐

Test 4: Sequences

Write the missing multiple in each sequence.

1. 2, 4, 6, 8, [ ], 12, 14, ...
2. 3, 6, 9, 12, 15, [ ], 21, ...
3. 5, 10, 15, 20, 25, 30, [ ], 40, ...
4. 10, 20, 30, 40, 50, 60, [ ], 80, 90, ...

Write the next three numbers in each adding 10 sequence.

5. 4, 14, 24, 34, 44, [ ], [ ], [ ]
6. 12, 22, 32, 42, 52, [ ], [ ], [ ]
7. 17, 27, 37, 47, 57, 67, [ ], [ ], [ ]
8. 26, 36, 46, 56, [ ], [ ], [ ]
9. 21, 31, 41, 51, 61, [ ], [ ], [ ]

Write the next three numbers in each subtracting 10 sequence.

10. 94, 84, 74, 64, [ ], [ ], [ ]
11. 85, 75, 65, 55, 45, [ ], [ ], [ ]
12. 79, 69, 59, 49, 39, [ ], [ ], [ ]
13. 73, 63, 53, 43, 33, [ ], [ ], [ ]

Mark your answers. How well did you do?

Mark [ ] out of 13 Time taken [ ]

Test 5: Addition facts (1)

Answer each question.

1. $3 + 4 = \square$
2. $4 + 5 = \square$
3. $5 + 2 = \square$
4. $7 + 3 = \square$
5. $6 + 4 = \square$
6. $1 + 8 = \square$
7. $6 + 2 = \square$
8. $3 + 5 = \square$
9. $5 + 4 = \square$
10. $9 + 1 = \square$
11. $7 + 2 = \square$
12. $4 + 4 = \square$
13. $3 + 6 = \square$
14. $5 + 5 = \square$

Fill in the missing numbers.

15. $8 + \square = 10$
16. $7 + \square = 9$
17. $\square + 3 = 10$
18. $\square + 6 = 9$
19. $3 + \square = 8$
20. $6 + \square = 8$
21. $\square + 9 = 10$
22. $\square + 4 = 9$
23. $4 + \square = 10$
24. $\square + 5 = 7$

Mark your answers. How well did you do?

Mark ☐ out of 24 Time taken ☐

Test 6: Subtraction facts (1)

Answer each question.

1. $10 - 7 = \square$
2. $10 - 9 = \square$
3. $9 - 2 = \square$
4. $8 - 6 = \square$
5. $10 - 8 = \square$
6. $7 - 5 = \square$
7. $9 - 3 = \square$
8. $8 - 5 = \square$
9. $7 - 3 = \square$
10. $10 - 4 = \square$
11. $8 - 4 = \square$
12. $9 - 5 = \square$
13. $7 - 4 = \square$
14. $10 - 5 = \square$

Fill in the missing numbers.

15. $6 - \square = 2$
16. $9 - \square = 3$
17. $\square - 3 = 5$
18. $\square - 5 = 5$
19. $6 - \square = 4$
20. $8 - \square = 3$
21. $\square - 4 = 3$
22. $\square - 4 = 6$
23. $7 - \square = 2$
24. $\square - 3 = 7$

Mark your answers. How well did you do?

Mark ☐ out of 24 Time taken ☐

Test 7: Addition facts (2)

Answer each question.

1. 3 + 7 = ☐
2. 4 + 8 = ☐
3. 5 + 6 = ☐
4. 7 + 6 = ☐
5. 6 + 9 = ☐
6. 6 + 8 = ☐
7. 9 + 2 = ☐
8. 3 + 8 + 7 = ☐
9. 5 + 7 + 2 = ☐
10. 9 + 3 + 6 = ☐
11. 7 + 5 + 7 = ☐
12. 8 + 8 + 5 = ☐
13. 6 + 8 + 7 = ☐
14. 5 + 9 + 8 = ☐

Fill in the missing numbers.

15. 8 + ☐ = 13
16. 7 + ☐ = 10
17. ☐ + 8 = 15
18. ☐ + 6 = 9
19. 6 + ☐ = 13
20. 6 + ☐ = 14
21. ☐ + 9 = 18
22. ☐ + 4 = 12
23. 7 + ☐ = 14
24. ☐ + 5 = 12

Mark your answers. How well did you do?

Mark ☐ out of 24 Time taken ☐

Test 8: Subtraction facts (2)

Answer each question.

1. $20 - 7 =$ ☐
2. $14 - 9 =$ ☐
3. $11 - 2 =$ ☐
4. $13 - 6 =$ ☐
5. $14 - 8 =$ ☐
6. $13 - 5 =$ ☐
7. $12 - 3 =$ ☐
8. $15 - 7 =$ ☐
9. $11 - 3 =$ ☐
10. $20 - 4 =$ ☐
11. $17 - 8 =$ ☐
12. $18 - 9 =$ ☐
13. $14 - 7 =$ ☐
14. $12 - 8 =$ ☐

Fill in the missing numbers.

15. $12 -$ ☐ $= 2$
16. $13 -$ ☐ $= 6$
17. ☐ $- 6 = 5$
18. ☐ $- 7 = 5$
19. $14 -$ ☐ $= 8$
20. $15 -$ ☐ $= 9$
21. ☐ $- 7 = 8$
22. ☐ $- 9 = 6$
23. $14 -$ ☐ $= 7$
24. ☐ $- 8 = 9$

Mark your answers. How well did you do?

Mark ☐ out of 24 Time taken ☐

Test 9: Mental addition

Answer each addition.

1. $26 + 3 =$ ☐
2. $34 + 2 =$ ☐
3. $23 + 5 =$ ☐
4. $33 + 4 =$ ☐
5. $41 + 6 =$ ☐
6. $62 + 7 =$ ☐
7. $35 + 5 =$ ☐
8. $75 + 6 =$ ☐
9. $41 + 9 =$ ☐
10. $46 + 6 =$ ☐
11. $54 + 7 =$ ☐
12. $88 + 5 =$ ☐

Fill in the missing numbers.

13. $82 +$ ☐ $= 87$
14. $32 +$ ☐ $= 39$
15. $24 +$ ☐ $= 28$
16. $33 +$ ☐ $= 37$
17. $31 +$ ☐ $= 39$
18. $27 +$ ☐ $= 32$
19. $48 +$ ☐ $= 56$
20. $46 +$ ☐ $= 51$
21. $67 +$ ☐ $= 75$
22. $86 +$ ☐ $= 92$

Mark your answers. How well did you do?

Mark ☐ out of 22 Time taken ☐

Test 10: Mental subtraction

Answer each subtraction.

1. 28 − 4 = ☐
2. 35 − 3 = ☐
3. 59 − 5 = ☐
4. 48 − 7 = ☐
5. 27 − 3 = ☐
6. 46 − 5 = ☐
7. 48 − 5 = ☐
8. 67 − 5 = ☐
9. 79 − 7 = ☐
10. 39 − 4 = ☐
11. 65 − 4 = ☐
12. 58 − 3 = ☐

Fill in the missing numbers.

13. 57 − ☐ = 52
14. 45 − ☐ = 41
15. 68 − ☐ = 62
16. 76 − ☐ = 71
17. 69 − ☐ = 60
18. 89 − ☐ = 85
19. 78 − ☐ = 74
20. 59 − ☐ = 52

Mark your answers. How well did you do?

Mark ☐ out of 20 Time taken ☐

Test 11: Written addition

Answer each addition.

1.
$$\begin{array}{r} 65 \\ +\ 23 \\ \hline \\ \hline \end{array}$$

2.
$$\begin{array}{r} 32 \\ +\ 16 \\ \hline \\ \hline \end{array}$$

3.
$$\begin{array}{r} 68 \\ +\ 21 \\ \hline \\ \hline \end{array}$$

4.
$$\begin{array}{r} 45 \\ +\ 34 \\ \hline \\ \hline \end{array}$$

5.
$$\begin{array}{r} 44 \\ +\ 23 \\ \hline \\ \hline \end{array}$$

6.
$$\begin{array}{r} 62 \\ +\ 25 \\ \hline \\ \hline \end{array}$$

7.
$$\begin{array}{r} 36 \\ +\ 53 \\ \hline \\ \hline \end{array}$$

8.
$$\begin{array}{r} 27 \\ +\ 71 \\ \hline \\ \hline \end{array}$$

9.
$$\begin{array}{r} 65 \\ +\ 25 \\ \hline \\ \hline \end{array}$$

10.
$$\begin{array}{r} 42 \\ +\ 27 \\ \hline \\ \hline \end{array}$$

Mark your answers. How well did you do?

Mark ☐ out of 10 Time taken ☐

Test 12: Written subtraction

Answer each subtraction.

1. $$\begin{array}{r} 69 \\ -\ 27 \\ \hline \end{array}$$

2. $$\begin{array}{r} 68 \\ -\ 46 \\ \hline \end{array}$$

3. $$\begin{array}{r} 89 \\ -\ 34 \\ \hline \end{array}$$

4. $$\begin{array}{r} 75 \\ -\ 43 \\ \hline \end{array}$$

5. $$\begin{array}{r} 98 \\ -\ 77 \\ \hline \end{array}$$

6. $$\begin{array}{r} 68 \\ -\ 33 \\ \hline \end{array}$$

7. $$\begin{array}{r} 95 \\ -\ 82 \\ \hline \end{array}$$

8. $$\begin{array}{r} 98 \\ -\ 26 \\ \hline \end{array}$$

9. $$\begin{array}{r} 75 \\ -\ 24 \\ \hline \end{array}$$

10. $$\begin{array}{r} 87 \\ -\ 34 \\ \hline \end{array}$$

Mark your answers. How well did you do?

Mark ☐ out of 10 Time taken ☐

Test 13: Word problems (1)

Answer each of these problems.

1. What is 18 take away 7? [ ]
2. Find the difference between 16 and 9. [ ]
3. What is the total of 8 and 7? [ ]
4. Subtract 5 from 13. [ ]
5. What is 12 minus 7? [ ]
6. What is 9 more than 47? [ ]
7. What is 8 less than 22? [ ]
8. Paul buys a pack of socks costing £6.
   How much change from £20 does he get? [ ]
9. 27 people are on a bus. 9 get off.
   How many people are on the bus now? [ ]
10. 42 people are on a bus. 7 more get on.
    How many people are on the bus now? [ ]

Mark your answers. How well did you do?

Mark [ ] out of 10 Time taken [ ]

Test 14: Multiplication tables facts 2s

Answer each question.

1. $6 \times 2 =$ ☐
2. $9 \times 2 =$ ☐
3. $3 \times 2 =$ ☐
4. $4 \times 2 =$ ☐
5. $2 \times 5 =$ ☐
6. $11 \times 2 =$ ☐
7. $8 \times 2 =$ ☐
8. $7 \times 2 =$ ☐
9. $2 \times 10 =$ ☐
10. $2 \times 2 =$ ☐
11. $12 \times 2 =$ ☐
12. $1 \times 2 =$ ☐
13. $2 \times 0 =$ ☐
14. $2 \times 6 =$ ☐

Fill in the missing numbers.

15. $2 \times$ ☐ $= 24$
16. $9 \times$ ☐ $= 18$
17. ☐ $\times 2 = 22$
18. ☐ $\times 10 = 20$
19. $5 \times$ ☐ $= 10$
20. $2 \times$ ☐ $= 16$
21. ☐ $\times 2 = 14$
22. ☐ $\times 2 = 12$
23. $2 \times$ ☐ $= 2$
24. ☐ $\times 2 = 0$

Mark your answers. How well did you do?

Mark ☐ out of 24 Time taken ☐

Test 15: Division facts 2s

Answer each question.

1. $6 \div 2 =$ ☐
2. $12 \div 2 =$ ☐
3. $18 \div 2 =$ ☐
4. $20 \div 2 =$ ☐
5. $16 \div 2 =$ ☐
6. $14 \div 2 =$ ☐
7. $2 \div 2 =$ ☐
8. $8 \div 2 =$ ☐
9. $10 \div 2 =$ ☐
10. $22 \div 2 =$ ☐
11. $24 \div 2 =$ ☐
12. $4 \div 2 =$ ☐

Fill in the missing numbers.

13. $20 \div$ ☐ $= 10$
14. $18 \div$ ☐ $= 9$
15. ☐ $\div 2 = 11$
16. ☐ $\div 2 = 7$
17. $16 \div$ ☐ $= 8$
18. ☐ $\div 2 = 5$
19. ☐ $\div 2 = 12$
20. $12 \div$ ☐ $= 6$
21. ☐ $\div 2 = 2$
22. ☐ $\div 2 = 4$

Mark your answers. How well did you do?

Mark ☐ out of 22 Time taken ☐

Test 16: Multiplication tables facts 5s

Answer each question.

1. $6 \times 5 =$ ☐
2. $9 \times 5 =$ ☐
3. $3 \times 5 =$ ☐
4. $4 \times 5 =$ ☐
5. $5 \times 5 =$ ☐
6. $11 \times 5 =$ ☐
7. $8 \times 5 =$ ☐
8. $7 \times 5 =$ ☐
9. $5 \times 10 =$ ☐
10. $5 \times 2 =$ ☐
11. $12 \times 5 =$ ☐
12. $1 \times 5 =$ ☐
13. $5 \times 0 =$ ☐
14. $5 \times 7 =$ ☐

Fill in the missing numbers.

15. $5 \times$ ☐ $= 55$
16. $9 \times$ ☐ $= 45$
17. ☐ $\times 5 = 55$
18. ☐ $\times 5 = 40$
19. $5 \times$ ☐ $= 10$
20. $5 \times$ ☐ $= 35$
21. ☐ $\times 5 = 30$
22. ☐ $\times 5 = 15$
23. $5 \times$ ☐ $= 5$
24. ☐ $\times 5 = 0$

Mark your answers. How well did you do?

Mark ☐ out of 24 Time taken ☐

Test 17: Division facts 5s

Answer each question.

1. $30 \div 5 = \square$
2. $15 \div 5 = \square$
3. $45 \div 5 = \square$
4. $55 \div 5 = \square$
5. $40 \div 5 = \square$
6. $25 \div 5 = \square$
7. $5 \div 5 = \square$
8. $35 \div 5 = \square$
9. $50 \div 5 = \square$
10. $10 \div 5 = \square$
11. $20 \div 5 = \square$
12. $60 \div 5 = \square$

Fill in the missing numbers.

13. $50 \div \square = 10$
14. $25 \div \square = 5$
15. $\square \div 5 = 11$
16. $\square \div 5 = 7$
17. $30 \div \square = 6$
18. $\square \div 5 = 1$
19. $\square \div 5 = 12$
20. $15 \div \square = 3$
21. $\square \div 5 = 8$
22. $\square \div 5 = 9$

Mark your answers. How well did you do?

Mark ☐ out of 22 Time taken ☐

Test 18: Multiplication tables facts 10s

Answer each question.

1. $7 \times 10 =$ ☐
2. $9 \times 10 =$ ☐
3. $3 \times 10 =$ ☐
4. $4 \times 10 =$ ☐
5. $10 \times 5 =$ ☐
6. $11 \times 10 =$ ☐
7. $8 \times 10 =$ ☐
8. $6 \times 10 =$ ☐
9. $10 \times 10 =$ ☐
10. $10 \times 12 =$ ☐
11. $2 \times 10 =$ ☐
12. $1 \times 10 =$ ☐
13. $10 \times 0 =$ ☐
14. $10 \times 6 =$ ☐

Fill in the missing numbers.

15. $10 \times$ ☐ $= 100$
16. $9 \times$ ☐ $= 90$
17. ☐ $\times 10 = 10$
18. ☐ $\times 10 = 80$
19. $2 \times$ ☐ $= 20$
20. $10 \times$ ☐ $= 60$
21. ☐ $\times 10 = 0$
22. ☐ $\times 10 = 110$
23. $10 \times$ ☐ $= 120$
24. ☐ $\times 10 = 90$

Mark your answers. How well did you do?

Mark ☐ out of 24 Time taken ☐

Test 19: Division facts 10s

Answer each question.

1. $30 \div 10 =$ ☐
2. $110 \div 10 =$ ☐
3. $40 \div 10 =$ ☐
4. $100 \div 10 =$ ☐
5. $50 \div 10 =$ ☐
6. $10 \div 10 =$ ☐
7. $20 \div 10 =$ ☐
8. $60 \div 10 =$ ☐
9. $120 \div 10 =$ ☐
10. $70 \div 10 =$ ☐
11. $90 \div 10 =$ ☐
12. $80 \div 10 =$ ☐

Fill in the missing numbers.

13. $100 \div$ ☐ $= 10$
14. $10 \div$ ☐ $= 1$
15. ☐ $\div 10 = 11$
16. ☐ $\div 10 = 7$
17. $30 \div$ ☐ $= 3$
18. ☐ $\div 10 = 2$
19. ☐ $\div 10 = 12$
20. $90 \div$ ☐ $= 9$
21. ☐ $\div 10 = 8$
22. ☐ $\div 10 = 5$

Mark your answers. How well did you do?

Mark ☐ out of 22 Time taken ☐

Test 20: Multiplication tables facts 2s, 5s, 10s

Answer each question.

1. $6 \times 2 = \square$
2. $9 \times 10 = \square$
3. $3 \times 5 = \square$
4. $4 \times 10 = \square$
5. $4 \times 5 = \square$
6. $11 \times 2 = \square$
7. $8 \times 2 = \square$
8. $7 \times 5 = \square$
9. $5 \times 10 = \square$
10. $9 \times 5 = \square$
11. $7 \times 2 = \square$
12. $11 \times 10 = \square$
13. $12 \times 5 = \square$
14. $12 \times 2 = \square$

Fill in the missing numbers.

15. $4 \times \square = 20$
16. $9 \times \square = 18$
17. $\square \times 5 = 55$
18. $\square \times 10 = 10$
19. $5 \times \square = 10$
20. $8 \times \square = 40$
21. $\square \times 5 = 25$
22. $\square \times 10 = 120$
23. $12 \times \square = 60$
24. $\square \times 2 = 24$

Mark your answers. How well did you do?

Mark ☐ out of 24 Time taken ☐

Test 21: Division facts 2s, 5s, 10s

Answer each question.

1. $30 \div 5 =$ ☐
2. $12 \div 2 =$ ☐
3. $15 \div 5 =$ ☐
4. $40 \div 10 =$ ☐
5. $6 \div 2 =$ ☐
6. $90 \div 10 =$ ☐
7. $16 \div 2 =$ ☐
8. $45 \div 5 =$ ☐
9. $50 \div 10 =$ ☐
10. $60 \div 5 =$ ☐
11. $20 \div 2 =$ ☐
12. $110 \div 10 =$ ☐
13. $25 \div 5 =$ ☐
14. $24 \div 2 =$ ☐

Fill in the missing numbers.

15. $40 \div$ ☐ $= 4$
16. $90 \div$ ☐ $= 9$
17. ☐ $\div 5 = 11$
18. ☐ $\div 10 = 10$
19. $50 \div$ ☐ $= 10$
20. $45 \div$ ☐ $= 9$
21. ☐ $\div 5 = 11$
22. ☐ $\div 10 = 12$
23. $12 \div$ ☐ $= 6$
24. ☐ $\div 2 = 9$

Mark your answers. How well did you do?

Mark ☐ out of 24 Time taken ☐

Test 22: Word problems (2)

Answer each of these problems.

1. Share 40 between 10. ☐
2. What is 5 times 5? ☐
3. Multiply 6 by 2. ☐
4. Divide 30 by 10. ☐
5. What is 50 shared between 5? ☐
6. How many is 7 lots of 5? ☐
7. What is 11 multiplied by 2? ☐
8. Kim plants 20 trees into five identical rows.
   How many in each row? ☐
9. Mr Smith shares £24 equally between his two children.
   How much do they each get? ☐
10. Some children get into teams of 5. If there are 45 children altogether, how many teams are there? ☐

Mark your answers. How well did you do?

Mark ☐ out of 10 Time taken ☐

Test 23: Fractions

1 Tick which of these show one half shaded.

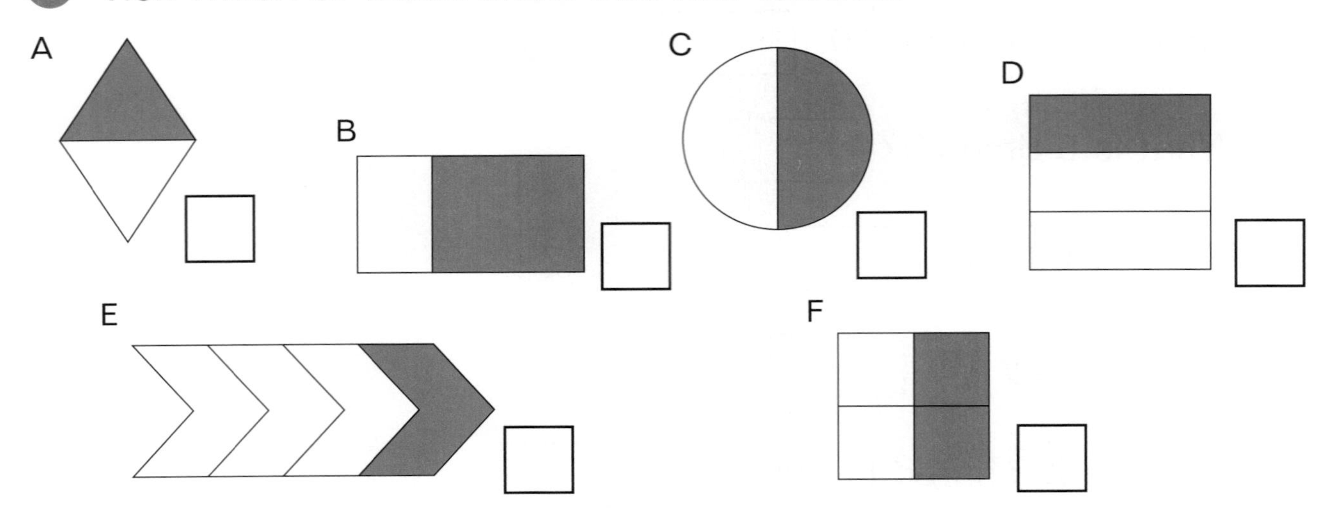

Write what fraction of each shape is shaded.

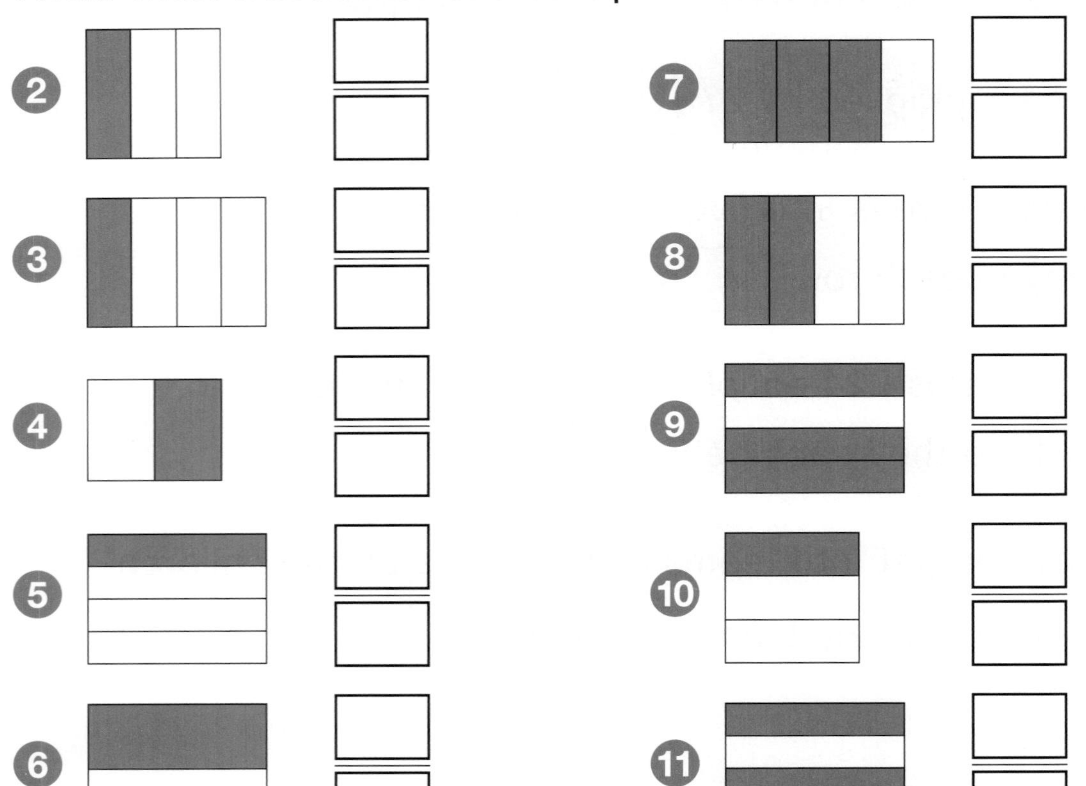

Mark your answers. How well did you do?

Mark ☐ out of 11　　Time taken ☐

Test 24: Fractions on number lines

Write what number each arrow is pointing to.

Include fractions in all your answers.

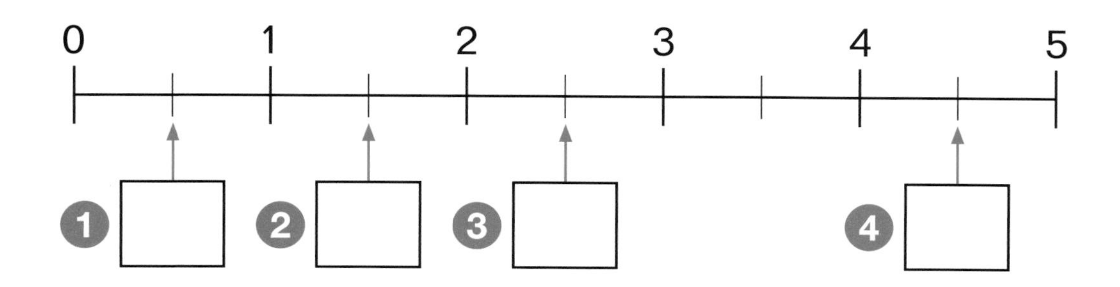

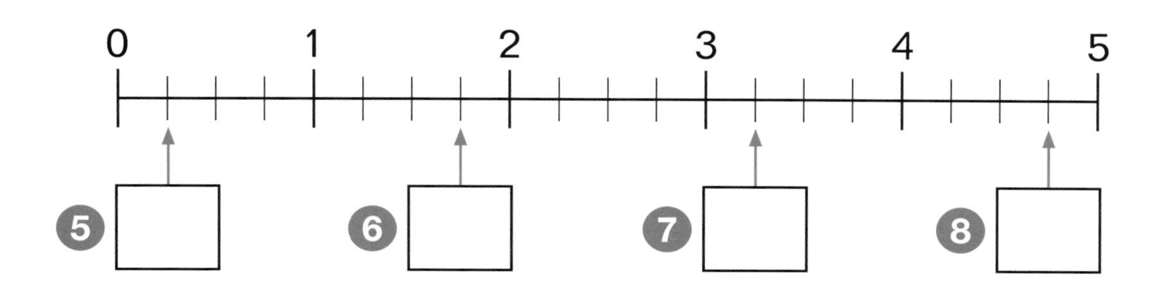

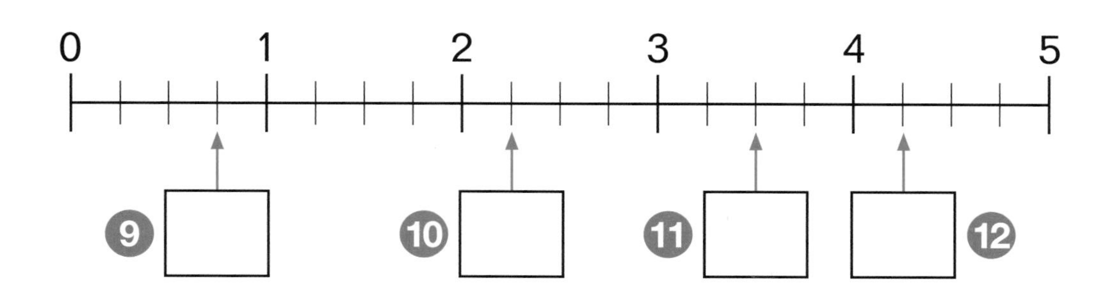

Mark your answers. How well did you do?

Mark ☐ out of 12 Time taken ☐

Test 25: 2D shapes

Name each shape.

1. 

2. 

3. 

4. 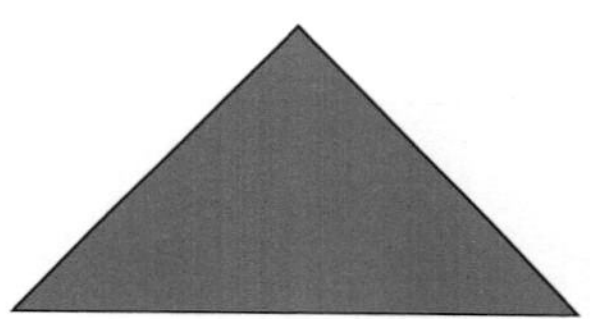

5. 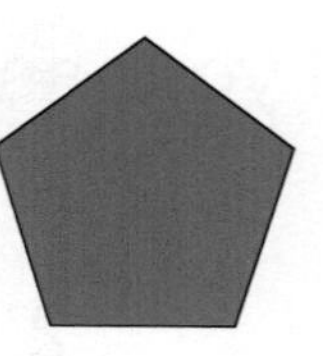

6. 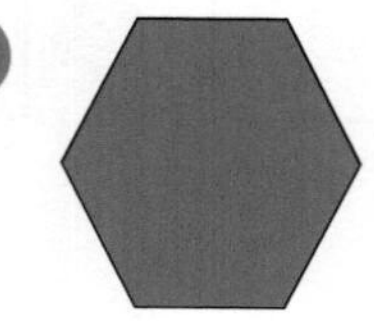

7. 

8. 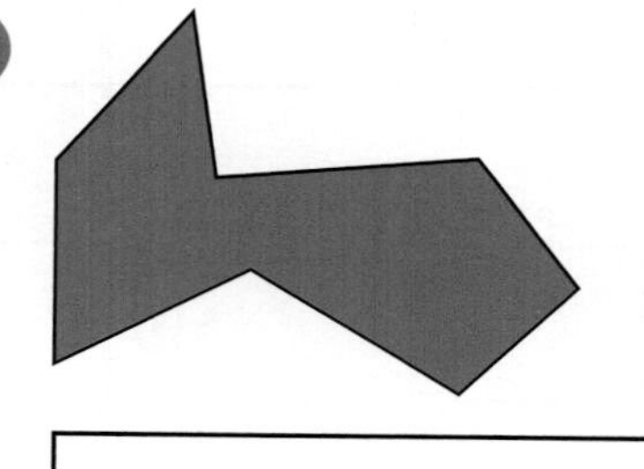

Mark your answers. How well did you do?

Mark ☐ out of 8 Time taken ☐

Test 26: Symmetry

Tick or cross to show whether the dotted line is a line of symmetry.

1 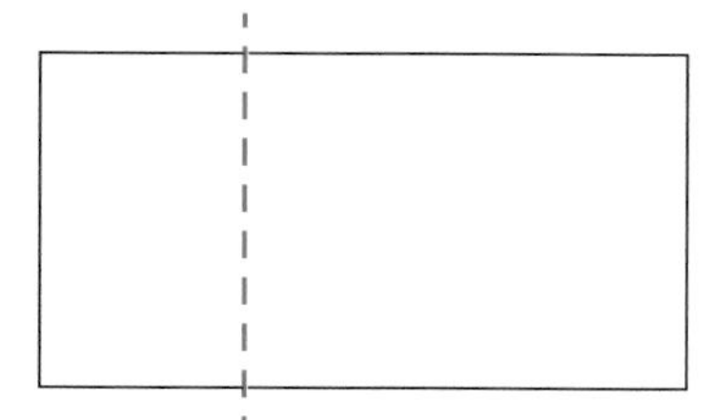

2 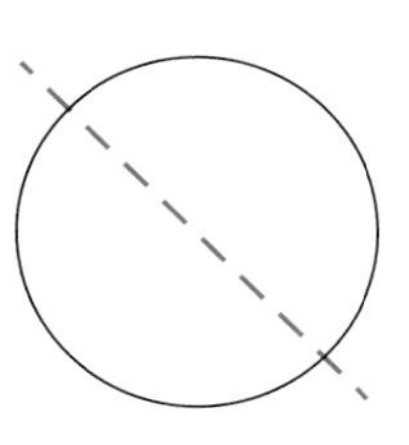

3 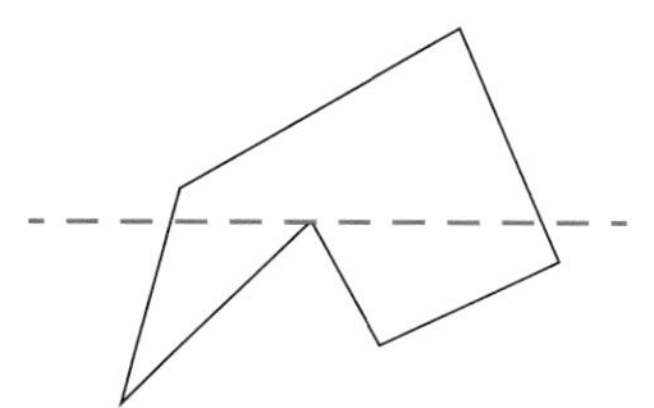

4 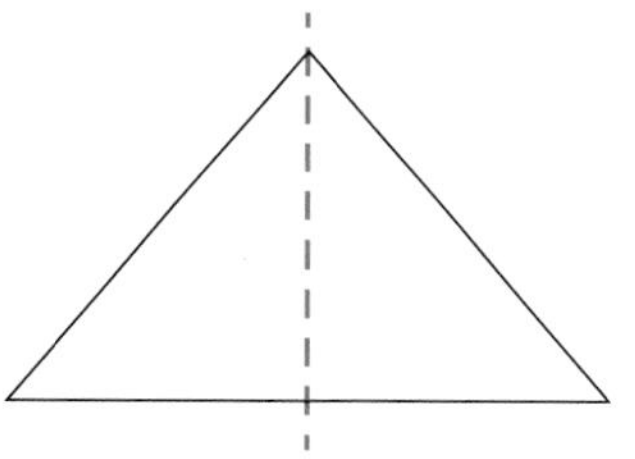

5 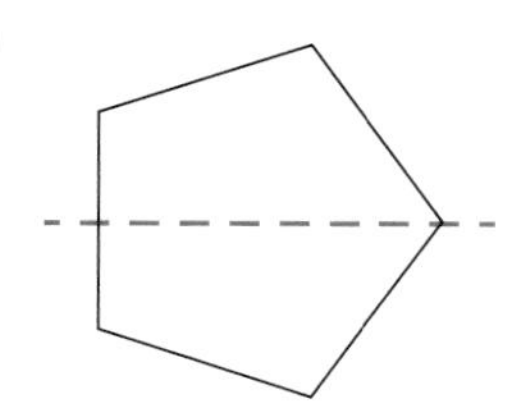

6 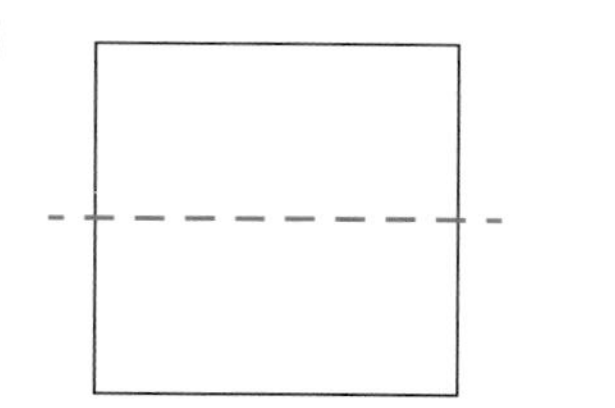

7 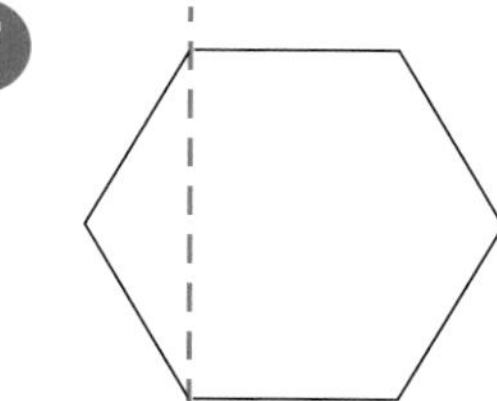

8 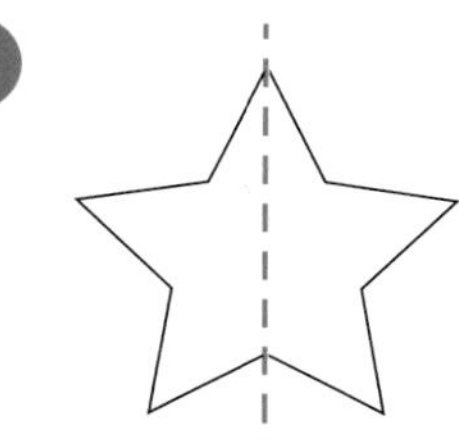

9 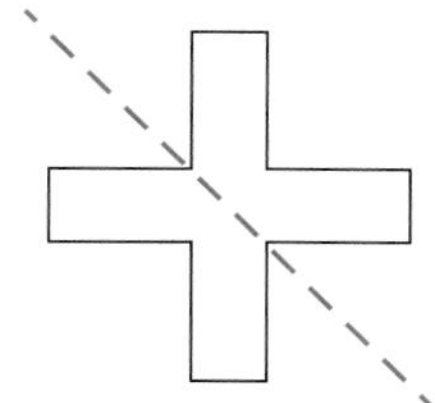

10 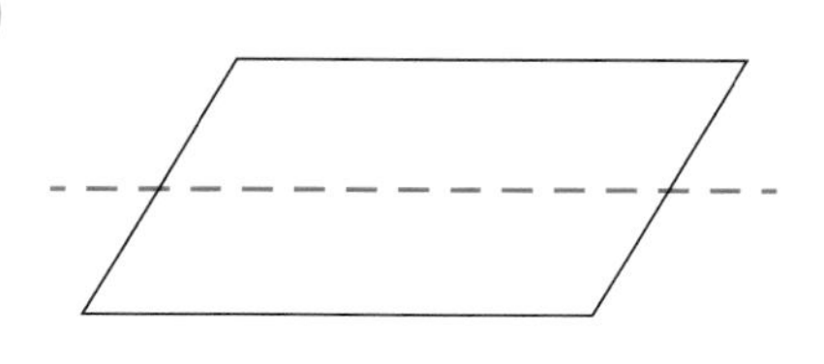

Mark your answers. How well did you do?

Mark ☐ out of 10 Time taken ☐

Test 27: 3D shapes (1)

Use the words in the box to name the shape shown in each picture.

cuboid	cone	cube	sphere	cylinder

1

2

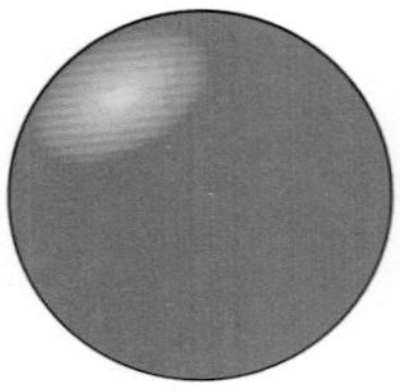

3

4

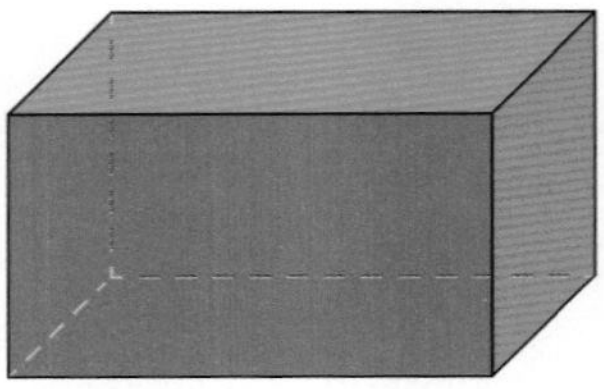

5

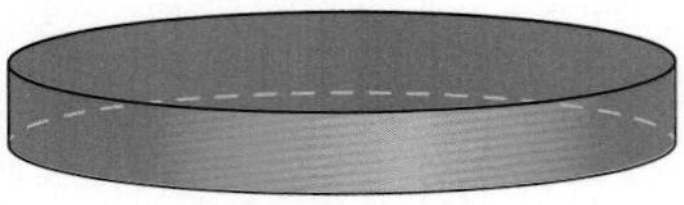

6

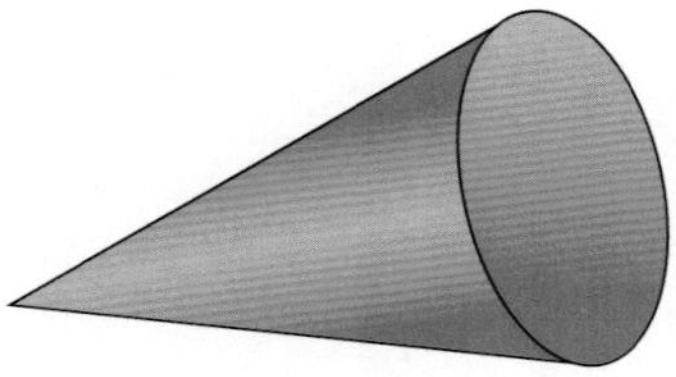

7

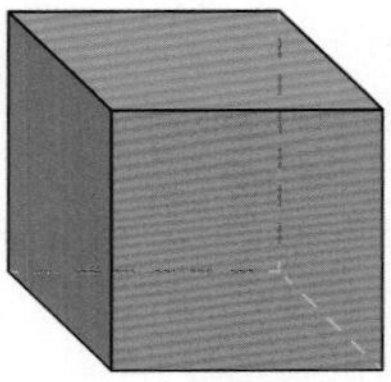

8

Mark your answers. How well did you do?

Mark ☐ out of 8   Time taken ☐

Test 28: 3D shapes (2)

How many faces has:

1. a cone? ☐
2. a cylinder? ☐
3. a sphere? ☐
4. a cube? ☐

How many edges has:

5. a cone? ☐
6. a cylinder? ☐
7. a sphere? ☐

How many vertices (corners) has:

8. a cone? ☐
9. a cylinder? ☐
10. a sphere? ☐
11. a cube? ☐

Mark your answers. How well did you do?

Mark ☐ out of 11 Time taken ☐

Test 29: Comparing 2D and 3D shapes

Tick the shape in each pair that has:

1. fewer sides

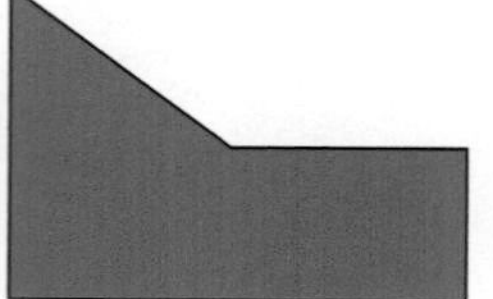

2. more vertices

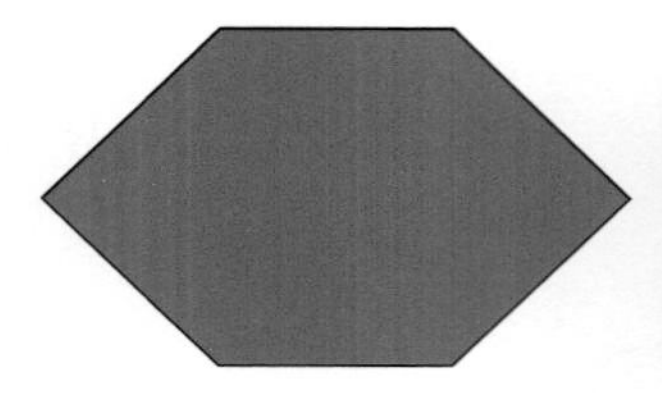
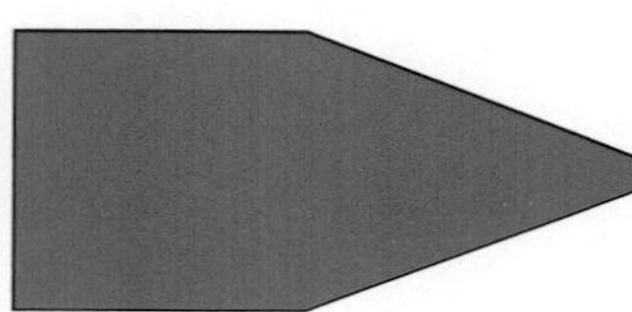

3. only straight edges

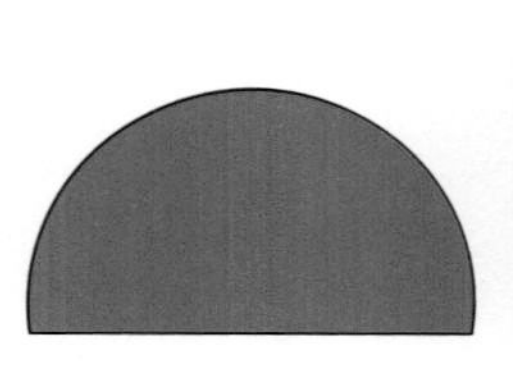

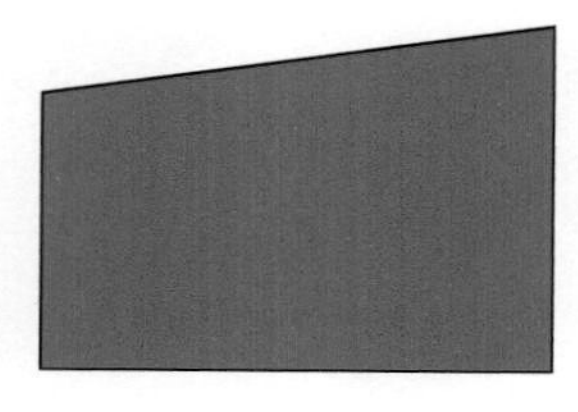

4. the smaller width

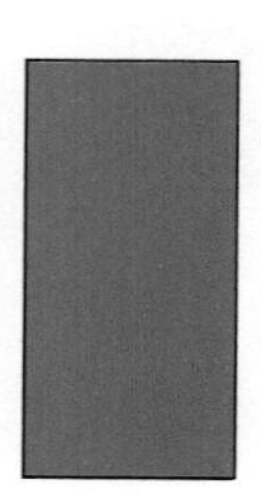

5. more faces

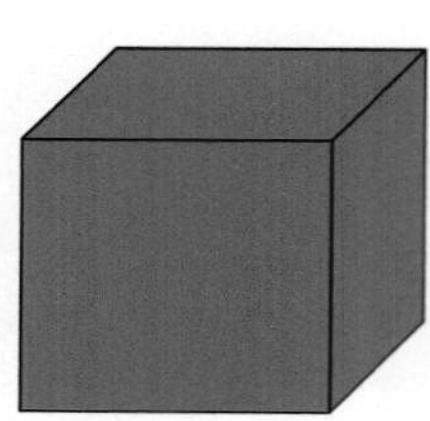

6. fewer circular faces

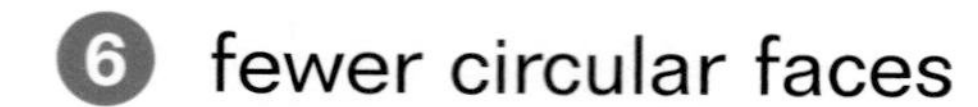
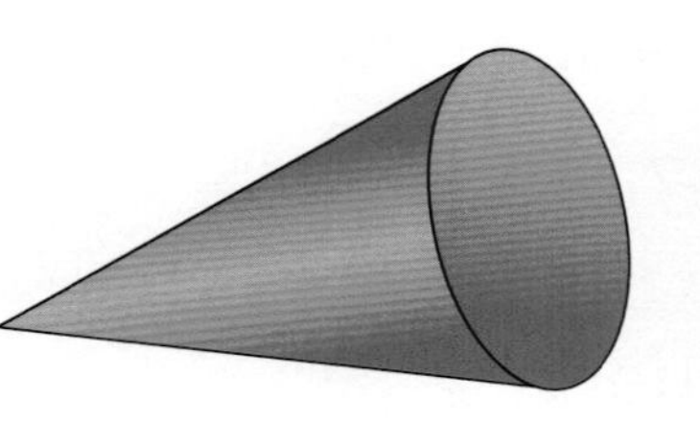

7. more vertices

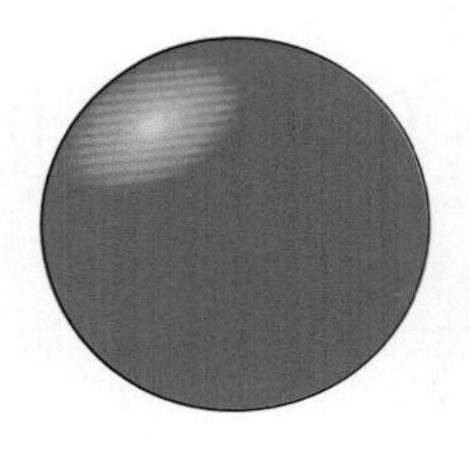
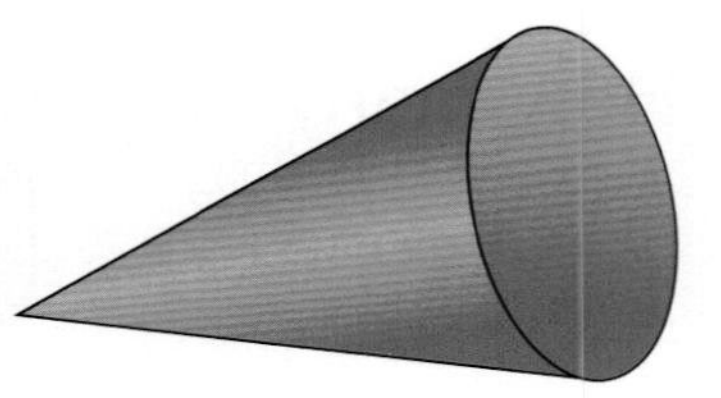

8. more edges

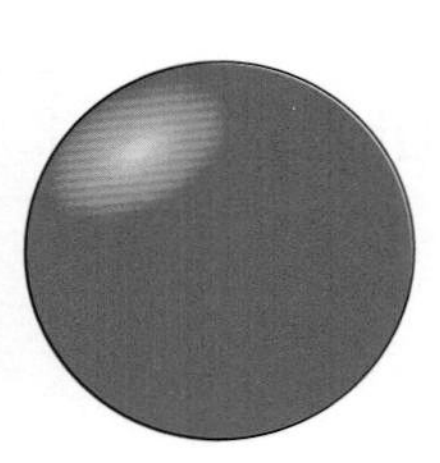

Mark your answers. How well did you do?

Mark ☐ out of 8 Time taken ☐

Test 30: Turns

Write whether the shape is turned through a **quarter** turn or a **half** turn to make the second shape.

1
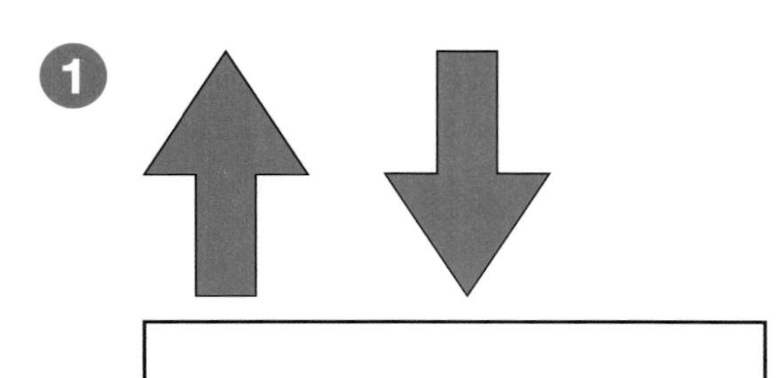

5
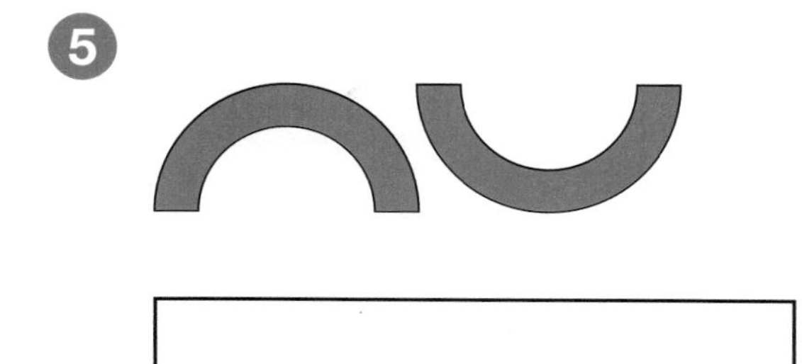

2

6
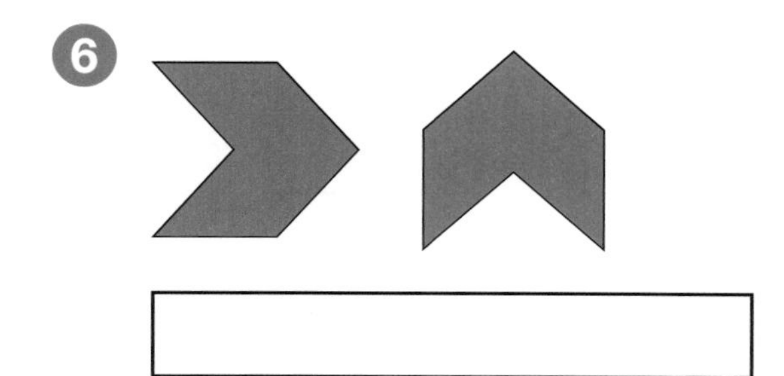

3
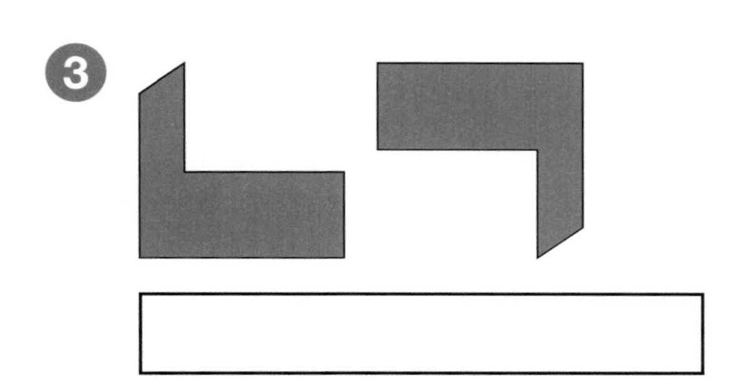

7
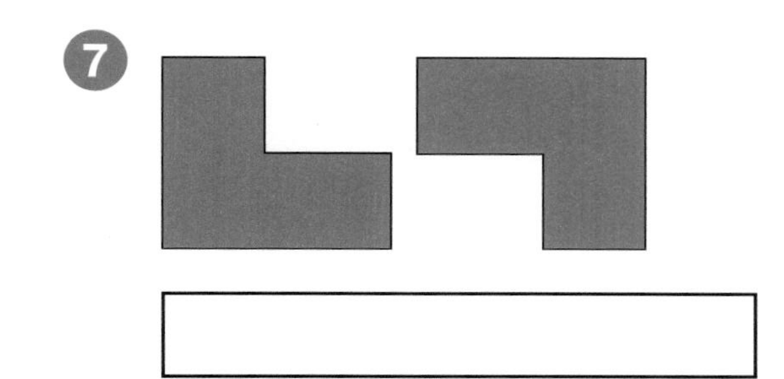

4
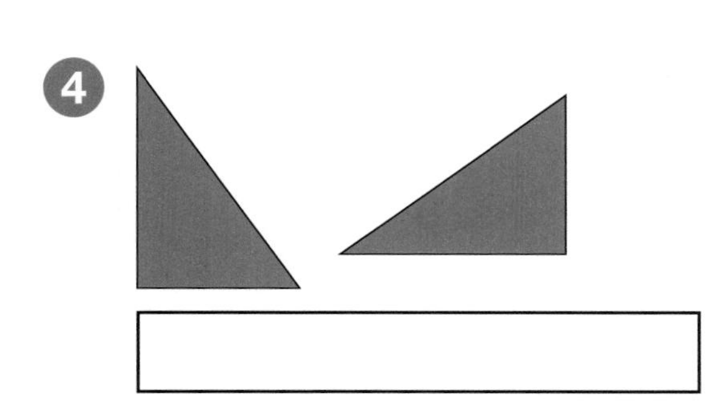

8
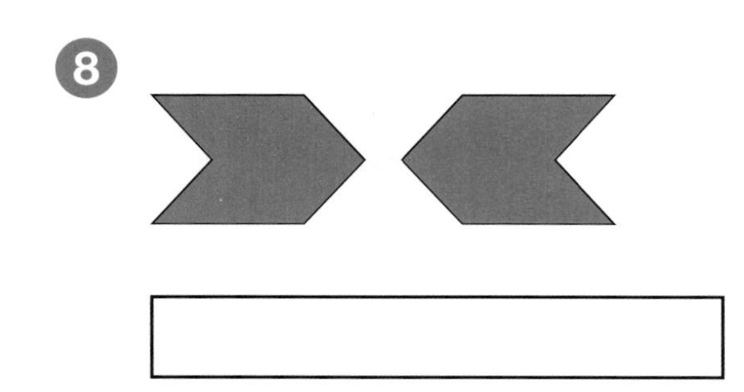

Mark your answers. How well did you do?

Mark ☐ out of 8 Time taken ☐

Test 31: Measuring length

Use a ruler to measure the length of each line.

1 ______ cm

2 ______ cm

3 ______ cm

4 ______ cm

5 ______ cm

6 ______ cm

7 ______ cm

8 ______ cm

9 ______ cm

10 ______ cm

11 ______ cm

12 ______ cm

Mark your answers. How well did you do?

Mark ☐ out of 12 Time taken ☐

Test 32: Comparing measures

Write < or > between each pair to show which is the longer length each time.

1. 50 centimetres □ 1 metre
2. 3 metres □ 2 centimetres
3. 2 metres □ 150 centimetres
4. 300 centimetres □ 2 metres
5. 101 centimetres □ 1 metre
6. 3 metres □ 200 centimetres
7. 10 metres □ 200 centimetres
8. $\frac{1}{2}$ metre □ 40 centimetres

Write < or > to show which is the heavier mass each time.

9. 150 grams □ 1 kilogram
10. 2 kilograms □ 300 grams

Write < or > to show which is the larger capacity each time.

11. 2 litres □ 300 millilitres
12. 4000 millilitres □ 3 litres

Mark your answers. How well did you do?

Mark □ out of 12 Time taken □

Test 33: Telling time (1)

Write these times using the words 'past' and 'to'.

1. 

2. 

3. 

4. 

5. 

6. 

7. 

8. 

9. 

10. 

Mark your answers. How well did you do?

Mark ☐ out of 10　　Time taken ☐

Test 34: Telling time (2)

Draw hands on the clocks to show these times.

1. quarter past two

2. quarter to seven

3. half past four

4. quarter past nine

5. ten to six

6. twenty-five past three

7. twenty-five to twelve

8. five past five

Mark your answers. How well did you do?

Mark [ ] out of 8 Time taken [ ]

Test 35: Telling time (3)

Write these times using the words 'past', 'to' or 'o'clock'.

1. 

6. 

2. 

7. 

3. 

8. 

4. 

9. 

5. 

10.  

Mark your answers. How well did you do?

Mark ☐ out of 10 Time taken ☐

Test 36: Coins and notes

Write the value of each coin or note.

1 

2 

3 

4 

5 

6 

7 

8 

9 

10 

11 

Mark your answers. How well did you do?

Mark ☐ out of 11 Time taken ☐

Test 37: Amounts of money

Write the total amount of money in each purse.

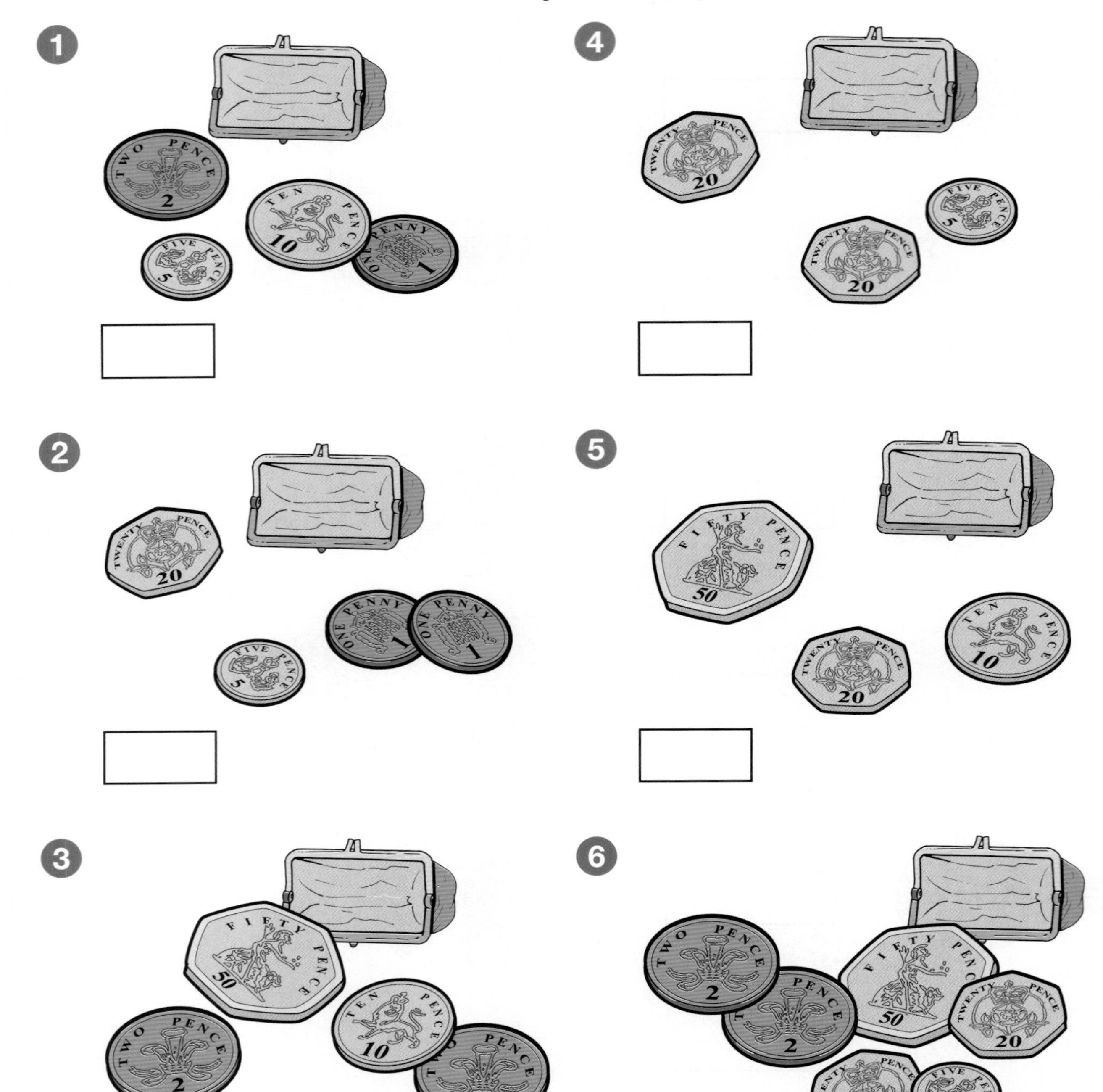

Mark your answers. How well did you do?

Mark ☐ out of 6 Time taken ☐

Test 38: Data handling

This pictogram shows the number of DVDs sold from each section in a shop on Saturday.

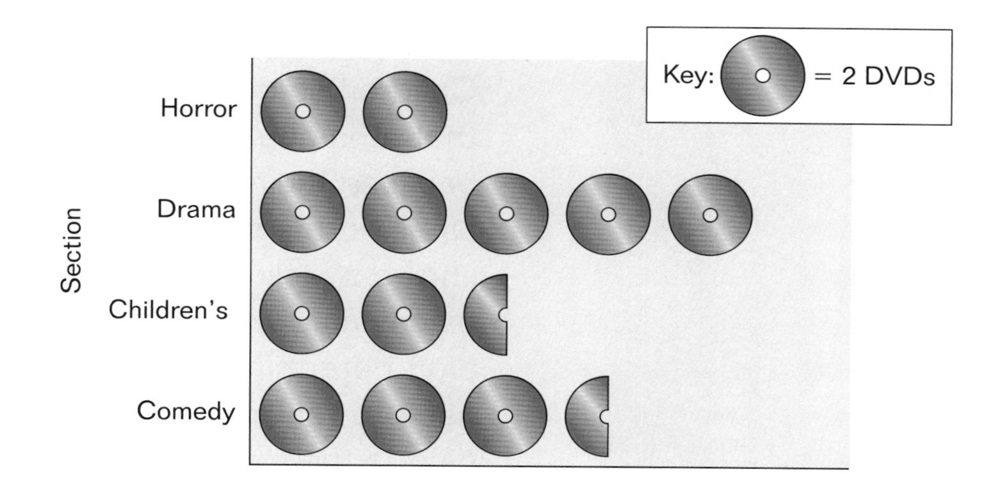

How many DVDs of each type were sold?

1. Horror [ ]

2. Drama [ ]

3. Children's [ ]

4. Comedy [ ]

5. How many more Drama DVDs were sold than Horror DVDs? [ ]

6. How many fewer Children's DVDs were sold than Comedy DVDs? [ ]

Mark your answers. How well did you do?

Mark [ ] out of 6 Time taken [ ]

Answers

Test 1
Encourage correct spelling. Note that children often incorrectly spell 'forty' as 'fourty'.

1 forty-eight
2 fifty-two
3 sixty-seven
4 forty-four
5 fifty-nine
6 ninety-three
7 eighty-six
8 97
9 21
10 68
11 87
12 70
13 45
14 17

Test 2
Children need to understand that the value of each digit in a number is different depending on its position.

1 40
2 8
3 50
4 2
5 60
6 80
7 6
8 70
9 80 + 2
10 90 + 7
11 60 + 1
12 70 + 6
13 67
14 43
15 28

Test 3
Children sometimes mistakenly think that a number is larger than another because they see larger digits, such as 9s, in the smaller number. This shows a lack of understanding of place value where the position of the digit determines its value. Children need to realise that the left-hand digit is the most significant because it represents the largest column, in this case tens, and so should be compared first.

1 47
2 78
3 88
4 98
5 82
6 92
7 87
8 93
9 14, 25, 32, 82
10 8, 21, 27, 50, 76
11 9, 62, 73, 89, 96
12 25, 42, 52, 54, 55
13 100, 86, 60, 43, 17
14 98, 94, 92, 76, 17, 7
15 89, 85, 58, 25, 12

Test 4

1 10
2 18
3 35
4 70

5 54, 64, 74
6 62, 72, 82
7 77, 87, 97
8 66, 76, 86
9 71, 81, 91
10 54, 44, 34
11 35, 25, 15
12 29, 19, 9
13 23, 13, 3

Test 5

1 7
2 9
3 7
4 10
5 10
6 9
7 8
8 8
9 9
10 10
11 9
12 8
13 9
14 10
15 2
16 2
17 7
18 3
19 5
20 2
21 1
22 5
23 6
24 2

Test 6

1 3
2 1
3 7
4 2
5 2
6 2
7 6
8 3
9 4
10 6
11 4
12 4
13 3
14 5
15 4
16 6
17 8
18 10
19 2
20 5
21 7
22 10
23 5
24 10

Test 7

1 10
2 12
3 11
4 13
5 15
6 14
7 11
8 18
9 14
10 18
11 19
12 21
13 21
14 22
15 5
16 3
17 7
18 3
19 7
20 8
21 9
22 8
23 7
24 7

Test 8

1 13
2 5
3 9
4 7
5 6
6 8
7 9
8 8
9 8
10 16
11 9
12 9
13 7
14 4
15 10
16 7
17 11
18 12
19 6
20 6
21 15
22 15
23 7
24 17

Test 9

1 29
2 36
3 28
4 37
5 47
6 69
7 40
8 81
12 93
13 5
14 7
15 4
16 4
17 8
18 5
19 8

9 50
10 52
11 61
20 5
21 8
22 6

Test 10

1 24
2 32
3 54
4 41
5 24
6 41
7 43
8 62
9 72
10 35
11 61
12 55
13 5
14 4
15 6
16 5
17 9
18 4
19 4
20 7

Test 11

1 88
2 48
3 89
4 79
5 67
6 87
7 89
8 98
9 90
10 69

Test 12

1 42
2 22
3 55
4 32
5 21
6 35
7 13
8 72
9 51
10 53

Test 13

Remind children, where necessary, to include the correct unit in their answers otherwise it is not correct.

1 11
2 7
3 15
4 8
5 5
6 56
7 14
8 £14
9 18
10 49

Test 14

Children of this age should learn their 2, 5 and 10 times tables up to 12 times each number.

1 12
2 18
3 6
4 8
5 10
6 22
7 16
8 14
9 20
10 4
11 24
12 2
13 0
14 12
15 12
16 2
17 11
18 2
19 2
20 8
21 7
22 6
23 1
24 0

Test 15

When learning their tables children should learn the related division facts also.

1 3
2 6
3 9
4 10
5 8
6 7
7 1
8 4
12 2
13 2
14 2
15 22
16 14
17 2
18 10
19 24

9 5
10 11
11 12
20 2
21 4
22 8

Test 16

1 30
2 45
3 15
4 20
5 25
6 55
7 40
8 35
9 50
10 10
11 60
12 5
13 0
14 35
15 11
16 5
17 11
18 8
19 2
20 7
21 6
22 3
23 1
24 0

Test 17

1 6
2 3
3 9
4 11
5 8
6 5
7 1
8 7
9 10
10 2
11 4
12 12
13 5
14 5
15 55
16 35
17 5
18 5
19 60
20 5
21 40
22 45

Test 18

1 70
2 90
3 30
4 40
5 50
6 110
7 80
8 60
9 100
10 120
11 20
12 10
13 0
14 60
15 10
16 10
17 1
18 8
19 10
20 6
21 0
22 11
23 12
24 9

Test 19

1 3
2 11
3 4
4 10
5 5
6 1
7 2
8 6
9 12
10 7
11 9
12 8
13 10
14 10
15 110
16 70
17 10
18 20
19 120
20 10
21 80
22 50

Test 20

1 12
2 90
3 15
4 40
5 20
6 22
7 16
8 35
9 50
10 45
11 14
12 110
13 60
14 24
15 5
16 2
17 11
18 1
19 2
20 5
21 5
22 12
23 5
24 12

Test 21

1 6
2 6
3 3
4 4
5 3
6 9
7 8
8 9
9 5
10 12
11 10
12 11
13 5
14 12
15 10
16 10
17 55
18 100
19 5
20 5
21 55
22 120
23 2
24 18

Test 22

1 4 each
2 25
3 12
4 3
5 10 each
6 35
7 22
8 4
9 £12
10 9

Test 23

A common error with fractions is to count the unshaded parts and give this as the denominator (the bottom number); for example, for the picture in question 3 children sometimes write $\frac{1}{3}$ rather than $\frac{1}{4}$ because three parts are unshaded. Remind children that the bottom number is the total number of equal parts.

1 Shapes A, C and F should be ticked. If a child incorrectly ticks the second shape point out that the two parts must be equal for this to show one half.

2 $\frac{1}{3}$

3 $\frac{1}{4}$

4 $\frac{1}{2}$

5 $\frac{1}{4}$

6 $\frac{1}{2}$

7 $\frac{3}{4}$

8 $\frac{1}{2}$ or $\frac{2}{4}$

9 $\frac{3}{4}$

10 $\frac{1}{3}$

11 $\frac{1}{2}$ or $\frac{2}{4}$

Test 24

1 $\frac{1}{2}$
2 $1\frac{1}{2}$
3 $2\frac{1}{2}$
4 $4\frac{1}{2}$
5 $\frac{1}{4}$
6 $1\frac{3}{4}$
7 $3\frac{1}{4}$
8 $4\frac{3}{4}$
9 $\frac{3}{4}$
10 $2\frac{1}{4}$
11 $3\frac{1}{2}$ or $3\frac{2}{4}$
12 $4\frac{1}{4}$

Test 25

1 rectangle
2 circle
3 square
4 triangle
5 pentagon
6 hexagon
7 hexagon
8 octagon

Test 26

1 ✗
2 ✓
3 ✗
4 ✓

5 ✓
6 ✓
7 ✗
8 ✓
9 ✓
10 ✗ (Children often think that this is a line of symmetry. It can help to cut a piece of paper this shape and fold it to demonstrate that it is not symmetrical.)

Test 27

1 cone
2 sphere
3 cylinder
4 cuboid (sometimes also called a rectangular prism)
5 cylinder
6 cone
7 cube
8 cuboid (sometimes also called a rectangular prism)

Test 28

1 2
2 3
3 1
4 6
5 1
6 2
7 0
8 1
9 0
10 0
11 8

Test 29

1

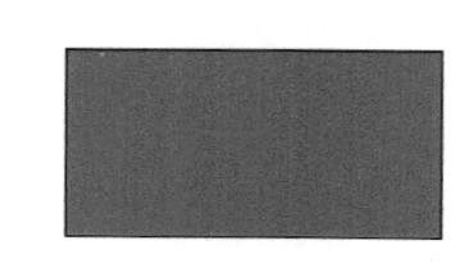

2

3

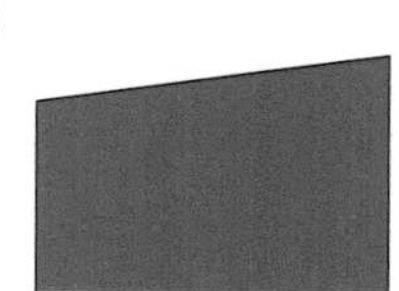

4

5

6

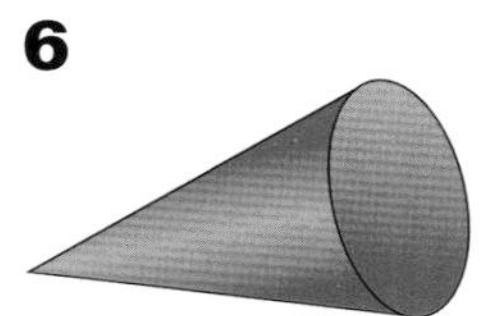

7

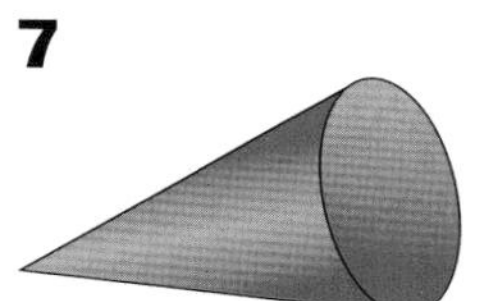

8

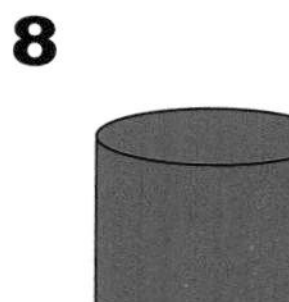

Test 30

1 half
2 quarter
3 half
4 quarter
5 half
6 quarter
7 half
8 half

Test 31

1 6 cm
2 9 cm
3 4 cm
4 8 cm
5 3 cm
6 12 cm
7 7 cm
8 14 cm
9 11 cm
10 5 cm
11 15 cm
12 13 cm

Test 32

1 <
2 >
3 >
4 >
5 >
6 >
7 <
8 >
9 <
10 >
11 >
12 >

Test 33

1 quarter past 5
2 quarter to 7
3 half past 11
4 quarter to 12
5 quarter past 4
6 five to nine
7 ten past six
8 twenty to one
9 twenty past four
10 ten to seven

Test 34

1 

2 

3 

4 

5 

6 

7 

8 

Test 35

1 quarter past 4
2 half past 5
3 8 o'clock
4 quarter past 10
5 quarter to 6
6 five past three
7 ten to eleven
8 twenty past nine
9 twenty-five to seven
10 ten past five

Test 36

Children should be reminded to give the unit (e.g. £ or p), otherwise it is not correct.

1 5p
2 10p
3 2p
4 20p
5 1p
6 50p
7 £20
8 £5
9 £1
10 £10
11 £2

Test 37

1 18p
2 27p
3 64p
4 45p
5 80p
6 99p

Test 38

Point out the key if the children give answers such as 3, 6 etc. Each DVD symbol represents 2 DVDs.

1 4
2 10
3 5
4 7
5 6
6 2